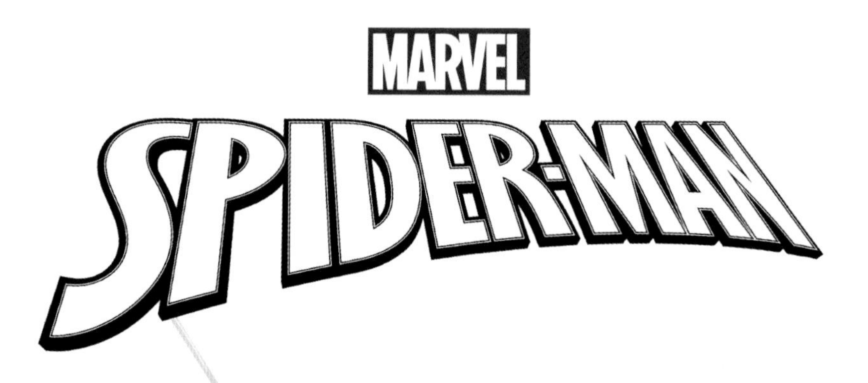

MILES MORALES TO THE RESCUE!

Written by David Fentiman

Senior Editor David Fentiman
Designer Stefan Georgiou
Production Editor Marc Staples
Senior Production Controller Louise Minihane
Managing Editor Sarah Harland
Managing Art Editor Vicky Short
Publisher Julie Ferris
Art Director Lisa Lanzarini
Publishing Director Mark Searle

Reading Consultant Maureen Fernandes

First published in Great Britain in 2020 by
Dorling Kindersley Limited
One Embassy Gardens, 8 Viaduct Gardens,
London SW11 7BW

Dorling Kindersley Limited,
A Penguin Random House Company
10 9 8 7 6 5 4 3 2 1
001–323478–Mar/2021

A CIP catalogue record for this book is available from the British Library.

ISBN: 978-0-24150-085-9

Printed and bound in China

For the curious

www.dk.com

This book is made from Forest Stewardship Council™ certified paper - one small step in DK's commitment to a sustainable future.

Contents

Meet Miles!

This is Miles Morales.
He lives in New York City.
Miles has a big secret!
He is really a Super Hero!

Spider-Powers

Miles got bitten by a spider.
The spider's bite gave him
lots of special powers.
Miles is now Spider-Man!

Miles can
climb walls!

Miles can
hide himself!

Miles is super strong!

Miles is super fast!

Miles in action

Miles shoots webs like a spider!
He can swing using his webs.
The webs are very strong.
Miles is not afraid of falling.

Miles and Peter Parker

Miles is not the only Spider-Man.
Peter Parker is a Spider-Man too!
Peter was bitten by a special
spider just like Miles.
They battle crime together.

Ghost-Spider

Miles and Peter Parker are
not alone as Spider-Heroes.
There are many others.
One of them is Gwen Stacy.
She calls herself Ghost-Spider!

Silk

Silk is another Spider-Hero.
She lives in New York City.
Her real name is Cindy Moon.
She can make silk webs and
shoot them from her fingers.

Spider-Heroes

Some villains are
too strong for Miles
to battle alone.
All of the Spider-
Heroes join together
to help him!

Miles' family

Miles lives with his parents.
Miles' mum is called Rio.
She is a nurse in the hospital.
Miles' dad is called Jefferson.
He is a police officer.

Rio Morales

Ms. Marvel

Miles has lots of friends.
One of them is Kamala Khan.
Kamala is a Super Hero too!
She calls herself Ms. Marvel.
She can stretch to any size.

The Champions

Miles' and Kamala's best friends are also Super Heroes! They have made a team called the Champions. They all have special powers.

Miles Morales
Exit 34-35
Bwa
Amadeus Cho
34 St
Viv Vision
Nova
Cyclops
Ms. Marvel

Amadeus Cho

Amadeus Cho is one
of the Champions.
He can turn himself
big and green!
He is very strong.

Viv Vision

Viv is another member
of the Champions.
She is really a robot!
Viv can fly and
walk through walls.

School

Miles goes to Brooklyn
Visions Academy.
His favourite subjects
are writing and art.
It is hard to do homework
and be a Super Hero!

ULTIMATE MATH
WHIP!

The Avengers

Sometimes Miles
joins the Avengers.
The Avengers are the greatest
Super Heroes on Earth.
Miles is always proud to
fight evil with them.

Falcon
Ms. Marvel
Iron Man
Captain America
Thor

Always ready

The world is a dangerous place. There are many selfish villains. Miles is always ready to swing into action!

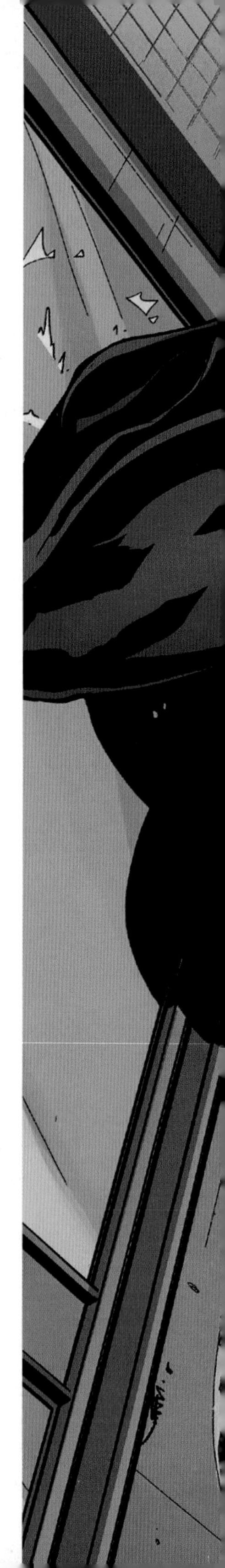

The Sinister Six

The Sinister Six are bad guys. They don't like Miles!

They always try to defeat him. The Sinister Six want to take over New York City.

Iron Spider

The Iron Spider is a thief.
He likes to steal things.
His suit of armour makes
him fast and strong.
Miles is faster and stronger!

Red Goblin

The Red Goblin is very evil.
He is a strong and
dangerous enemy.

Miles had to team up with Peter Parker to fight him. Together they defeated the Red Goblin.

Venom

Venom is an alien from space. He likes to cause trouble. Sometimes Venom and Miles work together as friends. Sometimes they are enemies!

Protector of New York City

Miles tries to keep his city safe. There are many bad people who want to hurt others. Miles must protect everyone.

Quiz

1. Is Miles super strong?

2. Where does Miles go to school?

3. What is Ms. Marvel's super-power?

4. How did Miles
get his super-powers?

5. Are the Sinister
Six good or bad?

6. Do Miles and Peter Parker fight crime together?

7. What is Miles' mum's job?

8. Where did Venom come from?

Answers on page 47

Glossary

Academy
a type of school

Defeat
to win against someone

Sinister
bad or scary

Super-power
being able to do something that most humans can't do

Super Hero
someone with super-powers who is good

Super Villain
someone with super-powers who is bad

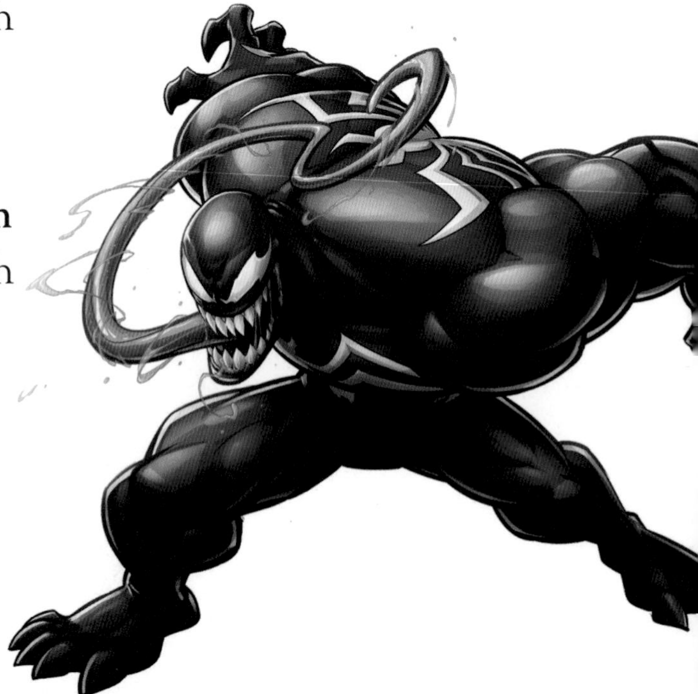

Index

Answers to the quiz on page 44–45

1. Yes 2. Brooklyn Visions Academy 3. She can stretch to any size 4. He was bitten by a spider 5. Bad 6. Yes they do 7. She is a nurse 8. He is an alien from space

A LEVEL FOR EVERY READER

This book is a part of an exciting four-level reading series to support children in developing the habit of reading widely for both pleasure and information. Each book is designed to develop a child's reading skills, fluency, grammar awareness and comprehension in order to build confidence and enjoyment when reading.

Ready for a Level 1 (Learning to Read) book

A child should:

- be familiar with most letters and sounds.
- understand how to blend sounds together to make words.
- have an awareness of syllables and rhyming sounds.

A valuable and shared reading experience

For many children, learning to read requires much effort, but adult participation can make reading both fun and easier. Here are a few tips on how to use this book with an early reader:

Check out the contents together:

- tell the child the book title and talk about what the book might be about.
- read about the book on the back cover and talk about the contents page to help heighten interest and expectation.
- chat about the pictures on each page.
- discuss new or difficult words.

Support the reader:

- give the book to the young reader to turn the pages
- if the book seems too hard, support the child by sharing the reading task.

Talk at the end of each page:

- ask questions about the text and the meaning of the words used – this helps develop comprehension skills.
- read the quiz at the end of the book and encourage the reader to answer the questions, if necessary, by turning back to the relevant pages to find the answers.